THE
Twelve Days
✳ OF ✳
Christmas

ILLUSTRATED BY

David Delamare

BARNES
&NOBLE
BOOKS
NEW YORK

On the first day of Christmas

my true love gave to me

A partridge in a pear tree.

On the **second** day of Christmas

my true love gave to me

Two turtledoves and a partridge in a pear tree.

On the third day of Christmas

my true love gave to me

Three French hens,

Two turtledoves, and a partridge in a pear tree.

On the **fourth** day of Christmas

   my true love gave to me

Four calling birds, three French hens,

Two turtledoves, and a partridge in a pear tree.

On the fifth day of Christmas

my true love gave to me

Five gold rings!

Four calling birds, three French hens,

Two turtledoves, and a partridge in a pear tree.

On the **sixth** day of Christmas

   my true love gave to me

Six geese a-laying,

Five gold rings!

Four calling birds, three French hens,

Two turtledoves, and a partridge in a pear tree.

On the **seventh** day of Christmas

   my true love gave to me

Seven swans a-swimming, six geese a-laying,

Five gold rings!

Four calling birds, three French hens,

Two turtledoves, and a partridge in a pear tree.

On the **eighth** day of Christmas

my true love gave to me

Eight maids a-milking,

Seven swans a-swimming, six geese a-laying,

Five gold rings!

Four calling birds, three French hens,

Two turtledoves, and a partridge in a pear tree.

On the **ninth** day of Christmas

my true love gave to me

Nine ladies dancing, eight maids a-milking,

Seven swans a-swimming, six geese a-laying,

Five gold rings!

Four calling birds, three French hens,

Two turtledoves, and a partridge in a pear tree.

On the **tenth** day of Christmas

  my true love gave to me

Ten lords a-leaping,

Nine ladies dancing, eight maids a-milking,

Seven swans a-swimming, six geese a-laying,

Five gold rings!

Four calling birds, three French hens,

Two turtledoves, and a partridge in a pear tree.

On the **eleventh** day of Christmas

   my true love gave to me

Eleven pipers piping, ten lords a-leaping,

Nine ladies dancing, eight maids a-milking,

Seven swans a-swimming, six geese a-laying,

Five gold rings!

Four calling birds, three French hens,

Two turtledoves, and a partridge in a pear tree.

THE TWELVE DAYS OF CHRISTMAS

On the twelfth day of Christmas

my true love gave to me

Twelve drummers drumming,

Eleven pipers piping, ten lords a-leaping,

Nine ladies dancing, eight maids a-milking,

Seven swans a-swimming, six geese a-laying,

Five gold rings!

Four calling birds, three French hens,

Two turtledoves,

And a partridge in a pear tree!

THE
Twelve Days
❄ OF ❄
Christmas

On the **first** day of Christmas my true love gave to me
A partridge in a pear tree.

On the **second** day of Christmas my true love gave to me
Two turtledoves and a partridge in a pear tree.

On the **third** day of Christmas my true love gave to me
Three French hens,
Two turtledoves, and a partridge in a pear tree.

On the **fourth** day of Christmas my true love gave to me
Four calling birds, three French hens,
Two turtledoves, and a partridge in a pear tree.

On the **fifth** day of Christmas my true love gave to me
Five gold rings!
Four calling birds, three French hens,
Two turtledoves, and a partridge in a pear tree.

On the **sixth** day of Christmas my true love gave to me
Six geese a-laying,
Five gold rings!
Four calling birds, three French hens,
Two turtledoves, and a partridge in a pear tree.

On the **seventh** day of Christmas my true love gave to me
Seven swans a-swimming, six geese a-laying,
Five gold rings!
Four calling birds, three French hens,
Two turtledoves, and a partridge in a pear tree.

On the **eighth** day of Christmas my true love gave to me
Eight maids a-milking,
Seven swans a-swimming, six geese a-laying,
Five gold rings!
Four calling birds, three French hens,
Two turtledoves, and a partridge in a pear tree.

On the **ninth** day of Christmas my true love gave to me
Nine ladies dancing, eight maids a-milking,
Seven swans a-swimming, six geese a-laying,
Five gold rings!
Four calling birds, three French hens,
Two turtledoves, and a partridge in a pear tree.

On the **tenth** day of Christmas my true love gave to me
Ten lords a-leaping,
Nine ladies dancing, eight maids a-milking,
Seven swans a-swimming, six geese a-laying,
Five gold rings!
Four calling birds, three French hens,
Two turtledoves, and a partridge in a pear tree.

On the **eleventh** day of Christmas my true love gave to me
Eleven pipers piping, ten lords a-leaping,
Nine ladies dancing, eight maids a-milking,
Seven swans a-swimming, six geese a-laying,
Five gold rings!
Four calling birds, three French hens,
Two turtledoves, and a partridge in a pear tree.

On the **twelfth** day of Christmas my true love gave to me
Twelve drummers drumming,
Eleven pipers piping, ten lords a-leaping,
Nine ladies dancing, eight maids a-milking,
Seven swans a-swimming, six geese a-laying,
Five gold rings!
Four calling birds, three French hens,
Two turtledoves,
And a partridge in a pear tree!

SIGNS AND SYMBOLS OF CHRISTMAS

(Can you find them in the paintings?)

Mistletoe- Regarded as a sacred plant by many ancient cultures. The Greeks used it to ward off evil. The Druids kept it, and all evergreens, in the highest regard, as they held the promise of renewal and everlasting life. Mistletoe became known as the "kissing bough," for during the holiday, a girl standing under its branches could not refuse a kiss.

Yule-log- This symbol was taken from the Norse festival of yuletide, which marks the winter solstice. At Christmas, it came to symbolize the warmth of the holiday and the joy of family. On Christmas Eve, the family would gather outside. A log, decked with ribbons and bows, would then be dragged inside to warm the family hearth.

Stockings- History is unclear as to the origin. Most likely, the hanging of stockings over the fireplace came from stories about the generosity of St. Nicholas, who lived in the fourth century. By the tenth century, Bishop Nicholas had become the patron saint of most of the European cities, and is still so to this day.

The Bundle Gift- Throughout Europe during the Middle Ages children would receive Christmas presents known as Bundle Gifts. The gifts came wrapped in cloth, and were bundled in threes. One gift would be a reward, another would be useful, and the last would be for discipline.

The Minstrel- The singing minstrels would wander through the city streets of Europe, singing carols, ringing bells, and giving blessings and good cheer for the holiday.

Horns and Bells- Young men in Europe during the Middle Ages would run through the streets, ringing bells and blowing horns to ward off evil and to celebrate each of the Twelve Days.

The Lord of Mischief (Misrule)- In England, a person would be chosen in a household or town to direct the festivals and gatherings over the twelve days. He would often gather a group of revelers together, dressed in costume and masks, and they would go from house to house singing songs and giving small gifts.

Painted Eggs- Beautifully painted eggs were given as gifts or for decoration (most notably in the Ukraine) during the holiday.

Geese- As well as hens, were thought to be good luck by the Europeans, for they were regarded as animals present at the birth of Jesus. A roasted goose is also the traditional Christmas feast in Europe, as the native turkey is in America.

Golden Wheat- Given to their livestock on Christmas for good luck, Europeans regarded wheat and hay as a symbol of the Nativity, when the baby Jesus was placed in a manger.

Cow's Breath- Legend held that the baby Jesus was kept warm in the stable by the breath of a cow. It was therefore thought to be good luck to see the frosty breath of a cow on a cold winter's morning.

Holly- First used in celebration by the Romans for the god Saturn, during the festival of Saturnalia. As Christians grew in number, the custom of hanging holly remained, and became part of the celebration of Christmas.

The Christmas Wreath- Like holly, the decking of evergreen boughs around the home was first introduced in pagan festivals. In 575, evergreen decoration was banned by the church as heathen ritual, but by the 1600s the custom was revived.

The Colors of Christmas- Red is the symbol for the blood of kinship, the bonding of family, and the act of charity. Green is the symbol of nature, the revel of youth, and the promise of eternal life. White is the symbol for purity, joy, and light. Gold is the symbol for that which is most holy and most precious.

The Christmas Rose- Like the poinsettia, the Christmas rose blooms in winter. Native to the mountains of Central Europe, the English imported the white flower to grow in celebration of the birth of Jesus.

Fireworks- In Australia and many parts of Europe fireworks explode in celebration on Christmas Day.

The Christmas Star- Stars have been held in special regard by almost every culture and religion, and for the Christian this is no less true. The five-pointed star represents the Star of Bethlehem, recounted in the Bible as the star that guided the Magi to the birthplace of the savior.

The Christmas Tree- The origin of the first Christmas tree was probably in the Black Forest of Germany. The fir tree would be decorated with fruits, nuts, and candles to mark the beginning of the winter festival.

THE TWELVE DAYS OF CHRISTMAS

A HISTORY

The Twelve Days of Christmas were declared a religious holiday throughout Europe in 567. The holiday lasted from Christmas Day on December 25 through the Epiphany on January 6. The Epiphany is the date given when the three Magi (wise men) found the baby Jesus and offered their gifts of gold, frankincense, and myrrh.

The holiday arose to replace the more ancient winter celebrations of the Roman festival, Saturnalia, in honor of Saturn, god of the harvest, and the Norse yuletide festivals, marking the winter solstice. The church, unable to place an exact date for the birth of Jesus, chose December 25 for Christ's Mass, or feast day. Instead of celebrating the harvesting of crops or the coming of winter, the birth of Christ was now celebrated. The people of Europe readily accepted this change, and the twelve days became a time of feasting, giving, and celebration. They would often hire or appoint a person in a village to be The Lord of Mischief. His job was to plan all the parties and festivals for the community, as well as gather young men to go through the streets at night in costume, giving out small gifts and singing songs. With the coming of the Industrial Revolution in the 1700s, the luxury of the long holiday disappeared, and now Christmas in most parts of the world is celebrated on one day only.

The Twelve Days of Christmas was a popular song during the Middle Ages. As a game song, one person would begin the first line, then another would join in, and then another, and so on. If a person missed a line he or she would give up a gift to the group.